Introduction

Tomatoes are the most important greenhouse
production is a very complex subject, demand

This booklet examines the economic consider
annual production cycle and then describes th
success. The UK industry is in direct competit
producers in Western Europe. It follows that the first requirement is
fruit which meets the high standards required by direct outlets.

There have been massive efforts in research and
development and this booklet presents them in a concise
and illustrative form. Although written for the commercial
grower there is much to interest the serious amateur.

Hydroponic methods of growing and pest and
diseases of tomatoes are particularly complex subjects
and have been omitted here. These can be studied in
other publications.

CONTENTS

		page
Economics		2
Monocrop or Rotation		3
The Crop Environment	What Should it be?	4-5
	How to Achieve it	6-8
	Fuel Saving	9
Varieties		10-11
Propagation	Sowing to Planting	12-15
Growing Media	Border Soil	16
	Peat	17
Nutrition	Base Dressing and Liquid Feeding	18-19
	Nutritional Problems	20
Watering		21
Growing-On	Training Systems	22-23
	Plant Populations	24
	Interplanting	25
Crop Management	Deleafing and Sideshooting	26
	Pollination	27
Harvesting	Picking to the Packhouse	28-29
	Grading	30
	Marketing	31
Further Reading		32

ECONOMICS

Before starting, restructuring or expanding any business a realistic BUDGET of COSTS and RETURNS must be essayed. This will reveal the likely margin of PROFIT – ie VIABILITY: it might indicate a LOSS.

RETURNS

Returns are the product of physical output x price received. A skilled grower can control physical OUTPUT – quantity, quality and continuity – reasonably well. PRICE will be very variable, according to OUTLET and SEASON as well as quality. In budgeting assume a 'reasonable' price. To pitch it too high is unrealistic and self deceiving; too low and the budget will show an unviable business. The assumed price will depend very much on OUTLETS (see p 31).

A BREAK-EVEN budget, showing the PRICE at which an average yield just breaks even is an excellent indicator of likely success.

COSTS

FIXED COSTS include the INTEREST and CAPITAL REPAYMENT (or DEPRECIATION) on capital expenditure – growing house, equipment and machinery. Then there will be WORKING CAPITAL, ie expenditure on LIVING COSTS, WAGES, FUEL, MARKET AND DISTRIBUTION, SPRAYS etc before any return is forthcoming. Working capital is usually provided by overdraft; and the INTEREST on this must be included.

PROFIT

Profit must provide for tax, and personal demands.

BUDGET EXAMPLE

A MARCH PLANTED CROP IN SOUTHERN ENGLAND

YIELD 18.5 tonnes/0.1 hectare.

RETURNS

May	June	July	Aug	Sept	Oct
£1100	3150	2000	1310	800	640

Total Returns	**£9000**

WORKING CAPITAL required for **GROWING COSTS** associated with the crop.

Marketing	£2100
Fuel	2200
Plants	870
Sterilisation — Me.Br.	240
Fertilisers	210
Pest and Disease Control	160
Sundries	330
Total Growing Costs	**£6110**
Gross Margin	**£2890**

PROFIT – or **LOSS** – is achieved by deducting **FIXED COSTS** from the **GROSS MARGIN.**

MONOCROPPING

(ie long season tomatoes involving use of heat) will generally be favoured in southern districts with natural advantages in winter light and warmth. These areas may be further from markets.

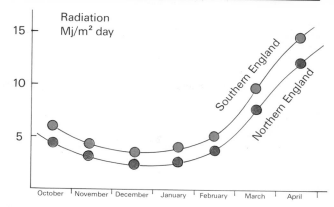

Monthly averages of daily solar radiation received at Efford EHS and Stockbridge House EHS.

Choose Monocropping if These Factors Predominate

1. Favoured natural climate for winter light and warmth
2. Modern aluminium greenhouse
3. East-west orientation
4. Well sheltered
5. Cheaper fuel
6. Local markets for early and other marketing advantages
7. Financial resources available for high working capital
8. Financial resources for full heating/insulation
9. High management skill
10. Skilled labour

Choose Rotation if These Factors Predominate

1. Less favourable climate
2. Wooden frame house
3. North-south orientation
4. Film plastic structures
5. Expensive fuel
6. Local direct outlets for a variety of produce.
7. Limited investment and working capital resources
8. Limited experience/managerial skill
9. Naturally fertile, well-drained soil for growing
10. Abundant casual, part-time labour

OTHER FACTORS

All light transmitting surfaces must be cleaned, at least annually.

Dust and smuts on exterior surfaces will restrict light transmission. Irrigation sprinklers on the greenhouse ridge are excellent for cleaning.

Natural or artificial windbreaks minimise structural damage and reduce heat loss.

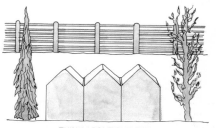

THINK ABOUT SHELTER

THE CROP ENVIRONMENT — WHAT SHOULD IT BE?

The crop environment in the growing house, from sowing to final harvest has a profound effect on crop performance and profitability.

TEMPERATURE

Air temperature is the main component influencing vegetative growth, truss form, flower number, fruit setting, fruit development, ripening and quality.

Minimum Night temperatures much below 12°C will markedly reduce growth and delay fruit ripening.

Maximum Daytime temperatures exceeding 30°C during cropping reduce plant vigour and yield and will adversely affect fruit quality. Temperatures above 26°C are uncomfortable for the work force.

Ideal Best results will obtain in the range 13°C – 16°C night and 20°C day. Root temperatures below 15°C are insufficient.

Temperature regimes are related to 5 stages of development

0 Sowing to pricking out

1 Pricking out to first truss just visible in head of plant

truss visible

2 Visible truss in head of plant to first flower opening

3 First flower opening, (normal planting stage) until two weeks after the start of picking

4 Two weeks after picking, to end of cropping
 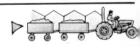

RECOMMENDED TEMPERATURES (°C)

Stage of Growth	0	1	2	3	4
°C Night Minimum	20	15	15	13-16	13-16
°C Day Minimum	20	20	18-20*	20	18
°C Ventilation Commencing	24	24	24	26†	21

* Planting before late February 18°C, planting after late February 20°C.
† 24°C If the crop is grown without CO_2 enrichment.

TEMPERATURE EXPERIMENTS

Experimental work has mainly been directed to Stage 3, as it is here that up to **two thirds of a season's fuel consumption** can be used. Trials have shown that 16°C night temperature in Stage 3 gives an earlier start to cropping and a higher early yield. Lower temperatures delay the start of picking, by about 3 days for every 1°C reduction in night temperature. The balance between value of fuel saved at 13°C and loss of early yield will depend on the relationship between fuel costs and early crop prices. Earlier sowings with a night temperature of 13°C in Stages 3 and 4 show promise.

Heat is often turned off on early planted crops from June to the end of September. Sunshine hours significantly affect day temperatures. Variation in weather and nursery location has been responsible for some variable trial results year to year.

CARBON DIOXIDE

Enrichment

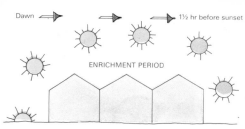

- Artificially lifting the level from 335 vpm (volumes per million) – normal out side air – to at least 1000 vpm, increases plant vigour, fruit number and size. Little is gained by having CO_2 levels above 1200 vpm.

- These effects become more marked as air temperatures are raised, and are proportional to the duration of enrichment.

- Begin enrichment as soon as seedlings are established after pricking off, until air temperatures make the operation uneconomic due to frequent ventilation.

- Early season CO_2 enrichment improves fruit 'set' under poor light conditions.

- CO_2 should be applied daily from sunrise to 1½ hours before sunset.

- Enrichment is of doubtful benefit for crops sown after the end of December.

HUMIDITY

Effects of different levels of relative humidity on crop performance are less understood. High relative humidities during the daytime can help setting.
High relative humidites at night, often associated with deposition of moisture on the plant as dew point is reached, can encourage disease.
Occasionally during the night and day greenhouse temperature fails to reach the set ventilation level, but remains above the level at which the heating thermostat demands heat. This is often referred to as the 'dead-zone'. To avoid disease infection and spread under these conditions, growers were advised to maintain minimum ventilation **or** pipe temperature. Both techniques increase fuel consumption. Today the remedy lies in good husbandry – keeping up with trimming, training, de-leafing and scrupulous hygiene. A fungicidal spray programme is also recommended.

- Many greenhouses have a slow, but natural air change depending on outside conditions. The use of insulation techniques, such as glass lap sealing or secondary glazing increases the relative humidity by reducing air changes.

THE CROP ENVIRONMENT – HOW TO ACHIEVE IT

TEMPERATURE AND HUMIDITY

Heating System

- The system must provide the required air temperature under all weather conditions. For heated crops this will mean a design capability giving a 22°C lift over outside temperature.
- The crop is sensitive to small differences in temperature, so temperature within the whole crop zone (vertically and horizontally) must be very uniform – within 0.5°C of the desired level.
- The installation should allow full use of mechanisation within the greenhouse, by careful positioning of heating pipes or ducts.

FUEL TYPE

Choice of fuel will have a critical effect on capital and running cost. Prices are volatile and subject to change. Coal is still the cheapest fuel, electricity the most expensive, with oil in between. Capital costs for coal installations are usually higher.

WHICH SYSTEM?

Steam

Direct steam may be used for heating purposes but unless the pipe layout is designed very carefully, undesirable temperature gradients can occur.

Hot Water

Small bore piped systems are to be preferred working at either low or medium pressure. Medium pressure systems need less pipework for a given heat output.

Air Heating

Ducted air heaters are suitable for mid-season crops; for those requiring lower temperature lifts; and for frost protection. They are not practical for early crops. Capital cost is less than that for pipe systems, but expensive light grade fuel oil has to be used. Also the benefit of radiant heat to young plants and soil is lost and savings in labour using pipes as rails for transport system are missing. Air heating systems should incorporate low level, film plastic ducting with spaced holes to give uniform heat distribution. Direct fired heaters using paraffin, light grade oil, or natural gas – ie combustion products entering the greenhouse – are successful provided temperature lifts are below 10°C. Also a useful amount of CO_2 is generated.

VENTILATION

The system should supply enough air to:
- prevent excessive air temperatures from natural radiation;
- replenish natural CO_2 levels;
- discharge excess moisture from plant transpiration.

Natural ventilation makes use of opening sections in the greenhouse roof. The opening area should be at least 15% of the floor area; 25% is ideal.

Forced systems are operated by fans and require air flows of 0.03 – 0.04 $m^3/sec/m^2$ of the floor area. Although fans may be useful in some circumstances, eg in houses with inadequate ridge ventilators, capital and running costs are heavy.

In most circumstances low cost natural ventilation, with automatic control (and manual control in the event of mechanical failure) is preferable.

CONTROL OF HEATING AND VENTILATION

There must be separate control of precise night, day and ventilation temperatures. The temperature sensors must be screened from the effects of radiation in an aspirated screen. A thermograph also in the screen, records temperatures so that performance of the heating system can be continuously checked. Calibration of the thermograph should be carried out at regular intervals.

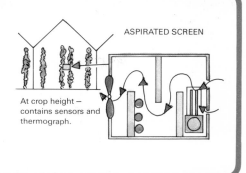

ASPIRATED SCREEN

At crop height – contains sensors and thermograph.

CARBON DIOXIDE – CO_2

Source and Equipment

There are two basic methods of enriching the atmosphere with CO_2 –

1. the use of pure gas itself, from a liquid or solid state;

2. the burning of hydrocarbon fuels, eg propane and paraffin.

PURE GAS

The advantages of pure gas are –
i it can be distributed in the greenhouse easily and evenly through small bore film plastic tubing between the double rows of plants; or through permanent plastic piping fixed to the greenhouse structure.
ii. pollution problems from burning hydrocarbon fuels are avoided.

To achieve the 1000 vpm target under average conditions requires an application rate of $5.6 g/m^2$ pure CO_2/hr.

LIQUID CO_2 (CO_2 gas liquified under pressure). Horizontal or vertical bulk storage tanks are available in capacities from 2-50 tonnes, and are suited to large enterprises.

12 or 22 kg cylinders are available, but the price is usually uneconomic in commercial use.

SOLID CO_2 This may be obtained in blocks and stored in a gasifier, a specially constructed cylinder with an electrically operated heater in the base.

PROPANE Commercial propane contains up to 33% propylene which is harmful to plants if unburnt fuel leakage occurs. Propane can be supplied in small cylinders, or in bulk for storage in tanks. Burning $2.2 g/m^2$ propane gas per hour will achieve 1000 vpm under average conditions. Two types of burner are available.

● Single, low cost, bar or ring burners. 25-50 per hectare will be needed according to output, design and shape of the house.

● A larger burner incorporating a fan, which gives more positive circulation of the CO_2.

PARAFFIN Suitable grades have a sulphur content below 0.03%. Burners may be free standing or suspended.

At current costs paraffin is the cheapest source and is particularly suitable for the smaller nursery and later planted crops.

NATURAL GAS Although an excellent source of CO_2 it is not generally available to growers in the UK.

CARBON DIOXIDE

Pollution Problems Burning Hydrocarbon Fuels

Without precautions, crop damage will occur –
- Use fuel with the lowest sulphur content that is economically practical.
- Relate the number of burners and their size to the area to be enriched.
- Do not 'push' undersized burners.
- Limit fuel consumption to that required for the desired CO_2 level. Check levels if any fuel conservation measures have been adopted.
- Check the performance of burners to ensure complete combustion.
- Avoid leaks of fuel gases from burners, mains and storage vessels.
- Use burners that have 'flame failure' devices.
- 'Purge' the atmosphere of tightly sealed greenhouses, especially film plastic structures, at least once a day, particularly when outside weather gives low rates of air exchange.

Aborting trusses and flower buds

affected

normal

EPINASTY

Necrosis and 'windowing'
SO_2 damage.

MEASUREMENT OF CO_2

- Equipment generating CO_2 should be set to give a constant rate of enrichment, and spot checks made to confirm the levels.
- Measurements should be taken under average wind conditions, in bright sunshine, towards midday, when the ventilators have been closed for some time.
- Inexpensive **gas detectors, using a hand pump** are satisfactory as are simple test kits based on **liquid colorimetric reagents**.
- Expensive **infra-red gas analysers** are appropriate to large enterprises and will continually monitor and adjust the desired level of CO_2.

COMPUTERS FOR ENVIRONMENTAL CONTROL

Now that computers are so much cheaper their use is justified on all but the smallest nurseries for accurate control and storage and retrieval of information. For example, a detailed record of air temperature can be obtained over any period (night and day), allowing the operator to assess the effectiveness of the heating system and to pinpoint faults.

Other useful detailed records can be monitored, for example –

Ventilation levels
CO_2 enrichment
thermal screens
irrigation systems
artificial illumination
and many more. . .

Careful interpretation of accumulated records could lead to the development of integrated, precisely controlled growing regimes for optimum production and profitability.

Fuel can be the highest production cost. Several types of insulation are available to reduce fuel costs. Numbers 5 and 6 may mean some greenhouse re-construction.

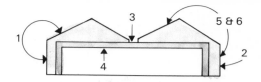

1 Lap Sealing

Large heat losses occur through glass laps – 20% when glass is dry and weather windy – and perhaps 10% over the year. **Silicone** sealants can be injected to produce a permanent flexible seal. The thinnest amount of sealant should be applied, when glass is dry. Lap sealing prevents glass slip, will seal glass to the gutter and join broken glass. **Lower** rates of CO_2 are needed to achieve 1000 vpm. Conversely humidities increase and under non-enriched circumstances CO_2 levels could fall below 335 vpm. The **cost is recovered** in 12-18 months with crops requiring high energy inputs.

2 Insulating the Side and Gable Ends

Lining the sides and doorways conserves energy and improves environmental uniformity. Air bubble or single sheet film plastic is used. Savings are **greatest** when there is an air gap between glass and insulating material. Heat requirements **drop** by 7-15% using air bubble and by 5-11% with single sheet film plastic – the saving depends on the ratio of insulated to total surface area. There will be some light loss. The financial benefit is **reduced** with low heat input regimes.

3 Gutter Insulation

Heat losses up to 9% occur through gutters. Materials such as polyurethane foam or moulded polystyrene reduce losses to 3%. They are sprayed, glued or clipped to the gutter. Harmful drips from condensation which cause crop damage are eliminated.

4 Thermal Screens

Annual fuel savings of 25-35% – depending on screen material – have been achieved. The effects on crop yield have been variable but some loss must be accepted. The **shadow** cast by the screens in the furled position and marked and sudden **changes** in environment at night and at dawn when screens are removed, probably account for these losses. Losses are **minimised** using thin clear film plastic and furling in an unobtrusive fashion. Newer fabrics (such as aluminised materials) can save **more** than 35% of fuel. If fuel costs continue to rise faster than returns, thermal screens could become essential for profitable early tomato production.

5 Secondary Glazing Systems

Completely lining with film plastic gives a 35% energy saving. At present materials and systems are developing rapidly. Melinex (a polyester film) used as internal or external secondary glazing has given savings of more than 40%. Humidities and CO_2 levels and inputs are changed.

6 Double Glazing and Glass Substitutes

Acrylic and polycarbonate materials can be used as partial or complete substitutes for glass but light transmission is inferior. 'Glazing' cost is 3-4 times **higher** than glass but glazing bars are reduced. Light loss is therefore not as high as might be expected. Two year's experimental evidence shows no yield difference on early heated crops under acrylic structures compared with conventionally glazed houses. Double glazing systems with two layers of polyethylene or 'Melinex' are also available.

New varieties are tested by ADAS each year on three Experimental Horticulture Stations. These trials are co-ordinated by the National Institute of Agricultural Botany. If a decision is taken to change varieties based on trial evidence, try them first in a small area. Some varieties are not yet available to the amateur but they are strongly recommended once they are released.

THE CHARACTERISTICS TO LOOK FOR

Yield

High total yield is important in all crops. Earliness is most significant for heated production. Some varieties are suitable for both heated and cold growing.

Fruit Shape

Modern varieties produce a high percentage Class I round fruit. Markets generally have a preference for 47-57mm diameter fruit. Some have to be down-graded for ribbing or boxiness and are not in the recommended list.

Plant Vigour

Where headroom is restricted, very tall varieties are unsuitable as fewer trusses are produced before the top wire is reached. Conversely, tall varieties often have extra vigour which can help them withstand adverse conditions.

Fruit Colour

Where fruit is picked and marketed before much colour has developed, 'greenback' may affect acceptability.

Disease Resistance

This is very important. A variety with a wide range of resistances simplifies crop management and reduces labour inputs needed to carry out control measures.

No variety susceptible to **Tomato Mosaic Virus** (TMV) is included in the list because resistance gives significant yield and quality advantages. Three strains of **leaf mould** (*Fulvia fulva*) occur in the UK. Two strains of *Fusarium Wilt* are recognised in the UK – one is rare. The varietal list shows resistance to *Verticillium Wilt* and **Brown and corky root rot**. At the moment there is no **good** variety with resistance to **Root-knot nematode** – with soil grown crops the only solutions are soil sterilisation or grafting.

Though not a disease, silvering (chimera) can cause problems. Firstly, small areas of stem and leaf are whitish green, quickly spreading to the whole plant, after which fruit setting ceases. Fruit develops discoloured (often raised) stripes and is downgraded.

PROMISING NEW VARIETIES

Goldstar

A tall variety, greenback and silvering free, for heated and cold houses. Disease resistance Tm2^2, C5, F2, V.

Marathon

A tall variety, greenback and silvering free for heated houses. Disease resistance Tm2^2, C5, F2, V.

E 7445

A tall variety, greenback free and suitable for heated and cold houses. It is not silvering free. Disease resistance Tm2^2, C4, F2.

STANDARD VARIETIES

Abunda A tall variety, greenback free and suitable for heated houses. Fruit is slightly firmer than average. Not silvering free. Disease resistance $Tm2^2$, C5, F2, V.

Ostona A tall variety, semi-greenback and suitable for cold houses. Very high yielding but prone to soft fruit in hot weather. It is not silvering free. Disease resistance $TM2^2$, C5, F1.

Piranto An intermediate variety, greenback free and suited to cold houses. It is fairly resistant to brown and corky root rot but is outyielded by other varieties when disease is absent. It is not silvering free. Disease resistance $TM2^2$, C5, F2, BRR.

Rovato A tall variety, greenback and silvering free, suited to heated houses. Fruit is slightly firmer than average. The variety is not suitable for wide spacings. Disease resistance $Tm2^2$, C5, F2.

Shirley An intermediate/tall variety, greenback free, suited to cold houses where it gives high yields. It is not silvering free. Disease resistance $Tm2^2$, C5, F2.

Sonatine A tall variety, greenback free and has proved a very reliable performer in heated and cold houses for five years. It is not silvering free. Disease resistance $Tm2^2$, C5, F2.

OTHER VARIETIES

Cherry Tomatoes

Varieties such as 'Gardeners Delight' are gaining popularity for direct sales and supermarket outlets. It is a greenback variety, lower yielding, but with an excellent flavour. The fruit size required is 25-35mm.

Beefsteak Types

There is increased demand especially from multiple stores. They are 'multi-locular' and are very fleshy.

The preferred grade is 67-82mm (BB). The best variety for late March to May plantings is Dombito. Marone is recommended for late planting only.

Different growing techniques have to be used:

- High levels of potassium and magnesium are required in base dressings.

- Wide spacing is necessary – 500-600mm in the row.

- Truss pruning is essential, reducing the numbers per truss to 3-5 when the fruit is 20mm diameter. The first fruit on a truss is often poor and is best removed.

- The fruit is easily damaged by dropping and fruit stalks can puncture adjacent fruit in market packs. The fruit cannot be machine graded or bulk handled and ideally needs marketing in trays with cell dividers.

11

PROPAGATION – SOWING TO PLANTING

Two proven ways of propagating tomatoes are described. To be successful attention must be given to **every detail** such as hygiene, timing, correct temperatures, watering, feeding and lighting.

The use of specialist plant propagators is increasing. This can be cheaper especially if a large house has to be heated when only a small area is needed for plant raising.

TIMING THE CROP

The timing for the first flower of 9 sowing dates using ADAS recommended temperatures in natural daylight.
This guide gives a basis for 12 month production.

Sowing Date	Flowering Date	
	South	North
5 October	19 November	–
20 October	15 December	–
1 November	1 January	26 January
15 November	25 January	10 February
30 November	12 February	22 February
15 December	22 February	5 March
30 December	3 March	15 March
15 January	15 March	25 March
30 January	28 March	2 April

THE SEED

Natural and pelleted seed are available. Natural seed is still the most popular with some growers using pre-germination techniques such as chitting, and fluid drilling into small containers to reduce handling. Whatever the source of seed, count the number of seeds per gramme (180-280), it will vary. Pre-sowing checks on percentage germination should be carried out. When sowing allow 25% for wastage.

COMPOST

Peat-sand composts are particularly suitable and can either be a low nitrogen proprietary type or mixed as follows:
Equal parts sphagnum peat and fine sand (0.5 – 1.0mm) to which is added –

Potassium nitrate	**0.4 kg/m^3**
Powdered superphosphate (19% P_2O_5)	**0.75 kg/m^3**
Ground chalk or limestone	**3.0 kg/m^3**

SOWING

Use new seed trays at least 50mm deep. Fill with moist compost, press down the corners, level and firm. 150-200 seeds are broadcast over the area. Cover with 5mm compost, lightly firm and water in with a fine spray to thoroughly wet the compost. Place glass over the box and cover with an opaque material.

Germination

Should be carried out in a closed environment using bottom heat giving a compost and air temperature of 20°C.

Seedlings emerge in 5 days, the boxes must then be immediately uncovered and placed on a bench with plenty of light.

It may be necessary to damp over the seedlings lightly to ensure the seed coat is sufficiently moist for cotyledons to break out.

Supplementary illumination (see p 14) can begin at this stage if the seed has been sown into small containers.

Pot Size

Container size is determined by the length of time that plants need to be in pots to ensure setting of lower trusses. Earliest sowings require 125mm pots containing 1.3 litres of compost. Size is reduced until March when plants are grown in 75mm pots holding 0.25 litres of compost. Labour requirement is 500 pots filled and pricked out per labour hour.

Compost

Proprietary composts can be used, or mixed as follows: 3 parts sphagnum peat to one part fine sand, or all peat medium grade to which is added –

Urea fomaldehyde	0.4 kg/m^3
Potassium nitrate	0.75 kg/m^3
Powdered superphosphate (19% P_2O_5)	1.5 kg/m^3
Ground chalk or limestone	2.25 kg/m^3
Magnesian limestone	2.25 kg/m^3
Trace element frit WM 255	0.4 kg/m^3

Pot Filling and Pricking Out

Bring the compost into the greenhouse before use to warm up.

Fill pots to top and lightly tap down. Ensure the compost is moist.

Use a dibber to make a hole deep enough to take the root without curling and allow the cotyledons to rest on the surface.

Do not firm in the seedling, just allow compost to fill round the hole.

Give frequent light waterings.

GRAFTING

GRAFT OPTIONS

R = Rootstock
S = Scion

Very stable. Fast grafting. Some check.

Bench graft. Fast grafting. Most check.

Potted 12mm apart. Slower grafting. Greatest success.

This is a well proven technique, especially where border sterilisation is impracticable. Rootstock varieties are available to the amateur.

Advantages: Save sterilisation costs – up to £3500 per hectare. Rootstocks Hires (Signaal) and Tm $KNVF_2$ give resistance to Brown and corky root rot, *Verticillium Wilt, Fusarium Wilt,* Root-knot eelworm (not Potato cyst eelworm) and TMV. It is vital that TMV resistant rootstocks are used with resistant scions.

Disadvantages: Demand for skilled labour at grafting time. 60 plants can be handled/hour. Rootstock germination is erratic and can produce 'rogues'. Excessive plant vigour can affect yield and quality especially on early crops.

The Method: Sow the rootstock 3-5 days earlier than the scion variety. Graft stems when 3-5mm thick and 50-80mm above soil level. Cut ½ to ¾ way through stem using a razor blade, the cut surface not more than 15mm. To hold the 'graft' together use 18mm clear, cellulose tape with a dispenser or use lead strip. Do not water graft union for a few days. After planting sever the scion roots if *Verticillium* or *Fusarium Wilts* are present in the borders.

THE PROPAGATION GREENHOUSE

The greenhouse must have good light transmission. It should have been thoroughly washed down with 2% formalin well before the house is to be used.

Plants can be propagated on open benches or on the border soil provided this is sterilised and warm.

Spacing

Pots are stood pot thick initially, finally moving to 300 x 300mm. The area of standing space rises from $160m^2$ to $900m^2$ per 10000 plants excluding paths.

At no time should leaves overlap. This is critical for early crops to avoid yield reduction.

Temperature and carbon dioxide enrichment are covered in the Crop Environment Section. (See p 4 and 5)

Lighting

Propagation period is reduced by 3-6 weeks using artificial illumination on seedlings and young plants. **In the North,** plantings up to end of February benefit. **In the South,** economic benefits are doubtful unless a number of batches are produced each season.

Lighting is used to delay the need for early sowing dates, not to advance crops.

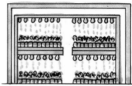

Replacement Lighting

The Techniques

1   Use in a greenhouse or growing room for light replacement. 2.4m fluorescent tubes spaced 150mm apart producing 15000 lux, double batched 12 hours on/off each day at 21°C.

2   Supplementary to natural daylight in a greenhouse. High pressure sodium lamps producing 8-11000 lux single batched 16 hours on each day, 20°C in light, 13-16°C in dark.

Supplementary Lighting

WATERING YOUNG PLANTS

After initial settling in, little water is required for at least a week.

Overhead spraying suffices until the first spacing; thereafter water should be directed into the pot.

Water requirement increases to 0.3 litres per plant as growth and daylight increase.

Large areas are probably best irrigated through drip irrigation lines.

During prolonged dull spells do not keep plants too wet. This can cause root loss, indicated by yellowing of lower leaves.

Feeding (See p 19).

PEST AND DISEASES

Problems likely to be encountered in the propagation stage are

Pests– Aphids, leaf miner, whitefly, red spider mite.

Diseases– Damping-off and root rot caused by *Pythium spp*, *Rhizoctonia solani*, *Phytophthora spp*.

STAGE OF PLANTING

This will vary according to time of year.

Plants more advanced than first truss in bud, need a 450mm split cane for support.

It is very important to remove the first truss shoot early to give strong truss development.

Before planting, 'off' types called 'Jacks', 'Rogues', or 'Christmas Trees' should be removed. Such plants take on a spikey appearance.

Strong truss shoot

first flower on first truss

Container Size		20mm fruit / 10mm fruit / Set / Flower / In bud / Visible — Stage of 1st truss — Container Size			
dia. mm	Volume litres				
125	1.4				
	1.2				
	1.0				
110	0.8				
	0.6				
	0.4				
75	0.2				
Planting Date	Southern England	January	February	March	April
	Northern England	January	February	March	April

GUIDE TO RECOMMENDED SIZE OF CONTAINER AND STAGE OF PLANTING AT DIFFERENT TIMES OF THE YEAR

PROPAGATION FOR LATE CROPS

Tomatoes may be planted in April-July often as a second crop. In these circumstances, with long days and very fast growth rate, a small pot or block are all that is required. Spacing is not critical. Large amounts of water are required by plants in small containers during the summer and overhead watering is suitable.

Instead of sowing seed, cuttings are sometimes used from TMV resistant material growing elsewhere on the nursery. Care must be taken to avoid bringing in pest or disease especially whitefly, red spider mite, *Didymella*, bacterial canker and 'silvered' cutting material

Side shoots are used for cuttings. They are put directly into a 75mm pot and placed on a mist bench or under a milky white polyethylene tent.

Rooting takes about 7 days and after a short weaning period, plants are grown in the usual way.

THE GROWING MEDIA

To achieve maximum production tomatoes need a well drained, well aerated growing medium, free from pathogens. Many crops are still grown in border soils, needing regular soil sterilisation. Over the last decade there has been a trend to growing in isolation from the borders, peat being the most popular medium.

BORDER SOIL

Soil Condition

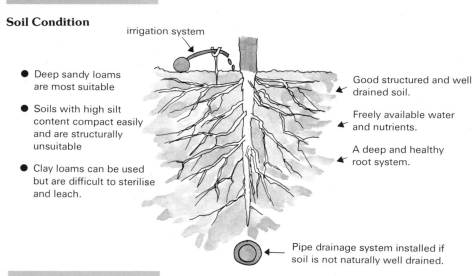

irrigation system

- Deep sandy loams are most suitable

- Soils with high silt content compact easily and are structurally unsuitable

- Clay loams can be used but are difficult to sterilise and leach.

Good structured and well drained soil.

Freely available water and nutrients.

A deep and healthy root system.

Pipe drainage system installed if soil is not naturally well drained.

SOIL PREPARATION

At removal of the previous crop note the health status of root systems and stems. Decisions can then be taken whether soil sterilisation is vital to the success of the next crop. Organic matter is essential for good physical condition – coarse and medium peats are the safest additives. Farmyard manure and mushroom compost are not recommended, as they can cause soft growth and poor fruit quality, and could contain damaging herbicide residue.

Analysis – Knowledge of the nutrient status of soils is vital. Analysis indicates pH, nitrogen, phosphorus, potassium and magnesium in the top 200mm of soil.

Sterilisation – The two methods of sterilising are by steam and chemicals. The high cost of sterilisation is the main reason for the increase in interest and commercial uptake of isolated growing systems.

Leaching – Analysis will show the total soluble salt (conductivity) of the soil. If levels are too high, growth is restricted and root damage can occur. Growth restriction is mostly likely on sandy soils low in organic matter; problems can be severe if these soils dry out. Leaching is recommended above ADAS conductivity Index 5, eg at Index 6 sandy soils require about 35 litres/m^2 and other soils 50 litres/m^2 water, (having brought soils to field capacity), to reduce to conductivity Index 2. An overhead irrigation system capable of uniform distribution, and adequate soil drainage, are essential for leaching.

Cultivation – The objective is the production of a deep, friable planting zone, free of compaction, with lime and fertilisers evenly distributed throughout. If compaction is found it must be broken by subsoiling. Alternating depth of cultivation will help. Rotavation of soils when wet is a common cause of poor structure.

PEAT GROWN

In most cases the peat is renewed for each crop, avoiding high sterilisation cost, but increasing material cost. Peat has the advantage of greater uniformity than soil, but much closer control of watering and nutrition is needed because of the smaller rooting volume and poorer nutrient retention of the compost. The most popular method is the peat bag or module, peat troughs less so. The economics of such methods are better for longer crops particularly monocrops.

Not less than 45 litres

lower cost/m² – more difficult to handle

Module Size and Peat Specification

Plastic modules are available in sizes to take 2 or 3 plants.

Not less than 24 litres

higher cost/m² – easier to carry

Both sphagnum and sedge peats are acceptable. There may be scope for reducing costs by the incorporation of bark or inorganic substances such as polystyrene granules.

The volume of growing medium must not be less than 12 litres per plant.

Modules are supplied with nutrient added and no base dressing is required.

Irrigation Systems

The rooting zone is very restricted compared with soil grown crops. It is vital therefore that irrigation systems give uniform water distribution. Extra nozzles may be required.

At planting the modules should be moist, not saturated.

Capillary matting placed under the modules, which have holes pierced in the bottom (instead of side splits) is an effective way of applying water and liquid feed.

Some modules, require slitting along the side after planting to avoid the accumulation of free water. Others allow water seepage through stitching at the bag end.

Watering up to four times a day, is required in the height of summer.

The Growing House and Planting

The modules should be laid on a firm level surface. It will help if the floor is landscaped to provide slightly elevated pathways which will remain dry and provide a firmer footing throughout the season. Soils are not sterilised and it is prudent to completely cover with white polyethylene sheeting. This prevents contamination by pathogens, improves hygiene during routine crop operations, and gives a light reflecting surface. It is advisable to use an insecticide under the sheeting to avoid subsequent damage from pests such as leaf miner.

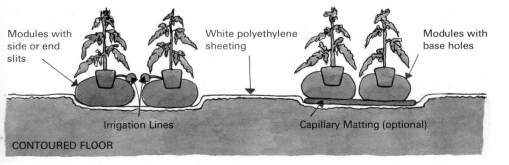

Modules with side or end slits

White polyethylene sheeting

Modules with base holes

Irrigation Lines

Capillary Matting (optional)

CONTOURED FLOOR

Tomatoes have high nutrient requirements, especially for **potassium** which is needed to produce good quality, flavoured fruit and balanced growth.

BASE DRESSING

Apply all of the **phosphorus** and **magnesium** needed for the whole season.

Apply part of the **potassium** requirement.

Nitrogen is not normally required pre-planting and never in steam sterilised soil.

Apply base dressings according to soil analysis and after any necessary leaching.

Apply evenly and incorporate thoroughly to a depth of 200mm.

On new greenhouse soils where potassium and magnesium levels are low incorporate up to $350g/m^2$ sulphate of potash and kieserite into the 200-400mm zone.

A Guide to Fertiliser requirements (g/m^2) at Different Soil Indices

FERTILISERS		N.P.K. Mg INDEX						
		0	1	2	3	4	5	Over 5
N Ammonium nitrate		30	15	Nil	Nil	Nil	Nil	Nil
P Triple super phosphate		150	140	130	110	80	45	Nil
K Sulphate of potash	planted before March	720	670	610	500	370	185	Nil
	planted after February	500	450	390	280	150	Nil	Nil
Mg Kieserite	planted before March	510	480	430	350	260	150	Nil
	planted after February	350	320	270	190	100	Nil	Nil

LIQUID FEEDING

Liquid feeds are applied from the early growth stages (4th true leaf) until 2-4 weeks prior to clearing the crop.

Feeds can be prepared from potassium nitrate, ammonium nitrate and in addition, for peat crops, mono-ammonium phosphate. Proprietary feeds are suitable provided they have **similar** N.P.K. ratios and are diluted to give nutrient concentrations close to those in the tables. The fertilisers are mixed with water to give a '**stock solution.**'

'Stock solutions' are very concentrated and could crystalise out if solution temperature falls below $10°C$. Further dilution will prevent this. They are then diluted to give the required strength. Diluters are of a displacement, compartment type, or use an injection pump principle. Dilution must be accurate and application uniform. Dilution strength can be checked using **portable conductivity meters**. Strength of feed is **critical** for peat growing where rooting volumes are small and margin for error slim.

Nutritional Problems (See p 20).

LIQUID FEEDS FOR BORDER GROWN TOMATOES

Growth Stage	Liquid Feed	The ingredients for 100 litres of stock solution		Nutrient concentration (mg/litre) at 1 in 200 dilution	
		Potassium nitrate kg	Ammonium nitrate kg	N	K_2O
4th leaf to ball watering	Low N	15	0	105	340
1st fruit swelling and thereafter	Medium N	15	4	180	340
Lacking vigour till plants recover	High N	15	7	225	340

It is possible to just use 180mg/litre N and 340mg/litre K_2O throughout cropping.

LIQUID FEEDS FOR PEAT GROWN TOMATOES

Growth Stage	Liquid Feed	The ingredients for 100 litres of stock solution			Nutrient concentration (mg/litre) at 1 in 200 dilution		
		Potassium nitrate kg	Mono ammonium phosphate kg	Ammonium nitrate kg	N	P_2O_5	K_2O
4th leaf to ball watering	Low N	15	Nil	Nil	105	0	340
Early crops to 2-5 wks after planting	Medium N	15	Nil	4	180	0	340
5 wks after planting thereafter	Medium N	19.5	2	2	180	60	450

Plants propagated in peat composts used for the dual purpose of seed sowing and potting will require phosphate as well as nitrogen and potassium. A suitable feed can be made using 100 litres stock solution containing 19.5 kg potassium nitrate and 2.0 kg mono-ammonium phosphate giving 140 mg/litre N, 60 mg/litre P_2O_5 and 450 mg/litre K_2O when diluted 1:200.

ANALYSIS DURING THE GROWING PERIOD

Border Grown
- Analysis taken during the growing period will prevent deficiency and crop loss.
- The critical phase is April to June. It is during this period of maximum cropping that potassium demand is greatest.

Peat Grown
- Peat analysis every 4 weeks is recommended. The critical period is April to June.
- Growers new to module growing are advised to have the peat analysed every 2 weeks during this critical period.

Potassium and magnesium are the most common nutrient deficiencies of tomatoes grown in soil. Deficiencies of calcium, boron, iron and manganese occur occasionally. Tomatoes grown in soil-less systems are more likely to suffer and need close control of the nutrient supply.

NUTRIENT DEFICIENCY: Typical Symptoms, Occurrence and Contributory Causes

POTASSIUM

Common: rarely affects yield. Poor quality fruit, uneven ripening mis-shapen, hollow fruit with low acidity and flavour. Excessive vigour in poor light periods.

Control: Apply base dressing of sulphate of potash according to soil analysis. High potassium liquid feeds can be beneficial.

MAGNESIUM

Common: rarely affects yield. Yellowing between veins –first on older leaves. High potassium aggravates deficiency. Root problems through waterlogging, disease, high conductivity, stress of heavy fruiting.

Control: High volume (1 litre/10m^2) sprays of 2% Epsom salts (plus wetter).

CALCIUM

More common in 'isolated' systems. Blossom end rot on fruit. Scorching of youngest leaves – following dull, humid weather. Aggravated by high conductivity and root damage.

Control: Liming border soils. Avoid ammonium N fertilisers, and high potassium/calcium ratios.

BORON

Common in propagation; often if planting delayed from loamless compost. Older leaves yellow towards tip. Veins are yellow or purple, leaves and stems brittle.

Control: Single soil drench of 10 ppm boron using 1g borax in 10 litres water; or 0.5 ppm boron in liquid feeds using 0.5g borax in 100 litres.

MANGANESE

Fine interveinal yellowing on older leaves. Confirm by leaf analysis. Aggravated by excess calcium in water or growing medium. Manganese toxicity can follow steam sterilisation of low pH soils.

Control: High volume sprays 4g/litre manganese sulphate plus wetter.

IRON

Yellowing then whitening of young leaves – veins remaining green. Usually induced by poor aeration of the growing medium.

Control: Improve root aeration. High volume sprays of iron chelate at 0.5g/litre plus wetter, ðr 0.05g/litre chelate (Fe-EDTA 6%) in liquid feed.

FIRST PRINCIPLES

Precision watering at all stages is a key factor for maximum production and fruit quality.

Requirements vary with –

Variations in solar radiation reaching the plant, according to season and greenhouse structural factors.

Plant requirements according to growth stage, eg a crop 1.2m high uses six times more than one 0.3m high.

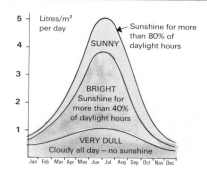

Calculation of Water Requirement

1. From measurement of total solar radiation at EHSs adjusted for local conditions.

2. From simple evaporimeters in the greenhouse.

3. From computer environmental control data, water needs can be calculated and controlled.

Water use should be checked by metering to match requirements.

Water Quality

Most mains and borehole supplies are suitable. Hard water, suspended solids, and high iron content all increase the risk of blockages in drip systems. Filtration, using 80-mesh screens installed on the downstream side of dilution equipment, helps. Water containing more than 200mg/litre chloride should not be used.

THE SYSTEMS

Many systems are used in tomato growing but whatever is chosen must: **Distribute** water uniformly, ie each outlet must give the same amount. **Be automated**, using sequence or moisture-sensitive controllers. Have easy access for **cleaning**. Be capable of use every day, and up to **4 times** a day in mid-summer.

Hose watering is now only used on small nurseries, or occasionally in the propagation stage and for 'ball-watering', ie the first watering after planting. Modern automatic systems reduce labour inputs.

Overhead Systems

These are the best method for leaching soils of harmful soluble salts, and for bringing soil to field capacity. Fairly high relative humidities are required to **prevent** 'dry-set' of tomato flowers and to **assist** pollination. Overhead systems (and hand damping) are ideal for this purpose. However they are less precise for irrigation than low level systems. Some late crops are grown using overhead systems.

Low Level Systems

These are the most precise and commonly used method of watering. Trickle irrigation systems of the screw thread or capillary tube type are most popular. There are newer and less costly systems using stitched polyethylene tubes, flexible plastic 'dual-tubes' or porous plastic tubes. Flexible plastic 'dual-tube' is more adaptable to changes in level and to long runs, without significantly affecting water distribution.

Successful systems of tomato training combine maximum yield and quality crops, with the most efficient use of labour. The system chosen will depend on many factors, the length of crop being of primary consideration. Interplanting has merit and will need to be considered.

FACTORS INFLUENCING THE CHOICE OF TRAINING SYSTEM

The Greenhouse   The height of the structure to the eaves determining top wire height and fixing, will be between 1.9m and 3.7m. A piped heating system can act as a wheel track for mobile steps. Mobile platforms with pneumatic tyres are available. These run on the greenhouse borders.

The Crop   A tomato plant will yield more heavily if:
- The terminal 1.5m of stem is in a near vertical position.
- The growing point is kept in the best light conditions.
- As many leaves are retained as possible, consistent with easy picking and disease control and maintenance of biological pest control agents.

Account should be taken of varietal vigour.

Labour   Labour is a high cost. It is important that staff can handle the crop easily and efficiently. One person should be capable of handling 5000 plants per week at summer peak periods. Labour will operate at maximum efficiency if excessive reaching and bending, and unnecessary walking are avoided.

WHICH SYSTEM?

All systems other than high wire layering are a compromise because of the multiplicity of factors to be taken into consideration.

The Basic Training System

Basic training is adequate for short term crops which are stopped at or soon after they have reached the top wire. Other methods have evolved from the basic training concept. They are designed to accommodate up to 10m of stem produced by long term crops. Plant arrangement and training is based on a double plant row with 1.6-1.7m between the centre of each double row.

After the planting holes have been taken out, polypropylene strings are tied to the top wire above the plant station. 300mm of string should rest on the soil surface and this is trapped in the hole at planting or tied to the plant base. The string is twisted in one direction round the plant – enough slackness must be allowed to perform the operation easily. Stringing should be carried out as soon as possible after planting.

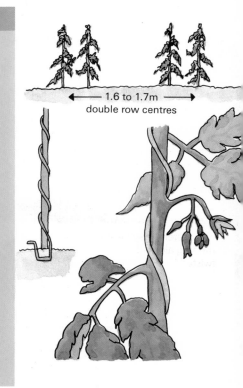

1.6 to 1.7m
double row centres

LAYERING SYSTEMS

All layering systems work on the principle that when the growing point reaches the top wire, the head of the plant is lowered. The most difficult period is at the time of first layering. A bottom wire keeps stems and fruits off the ground. This reduces disease problems, keeps fruit clean and helps picking. The string is usually wound round a bobbin (less commonly taken to the top wire through an 'S' hook and then along to the left – usually –and tied beyond a hook). The bobbin method takes better account of variable plant vigour When stringing, remember the length of growing season, which can produce 10m of crop growth.

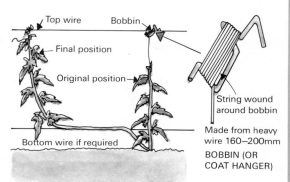

High wire layering is used where the top wire is at least 3m from the floor. Plant handling is carried out from mobile steps. The advantages of high wire layering are –more vertical stem, leaf left longer on the plant, positive damping, easier picking – all leading to higher yields.

MODIFIED GUERNSEY ARCH

The top wires are positioned between 1.9 and 2m at convenient worker height. The plants are taken over the path and then between the double row, securing the head of the plant to position A. As the plant grows, the stem falls between the double row and the head is fixed again at position A. This is a very demanding system as plants are overhead for much of the season.

DUTCH HOOK SYSTEM

The system may be summarised as arch training along the row. The plant is twisted in the normal fashion until it is 300mm from the top wire. Subsequent growth is laid over the hook alongside it. Further extension growth causes the head of the plant to hang down which can, at a later date be trained back up the stem of the next plant. A disadvantage is that the head of the plant is directed down, away from the light.

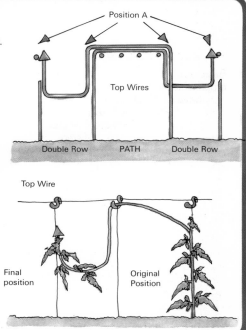

PLANT POPULATIONS

It is important that a grower chooses the optimum plant population for his circumstances. It should be as low as possible consistent with achieving heavy early and total yield, with good quality fruit, and of a size required by his market. Varietal characteristics especially plant habit and vigour must be taken into consideration. Experimental and grower results are variable due to location, the type of greenhouse, and especially year to year climatic variation in terms of early light. Spacings can vary between 2 and 3.6 per m^2 equivalent to 20000 to 36000 per hectare.

ADVANTAGES AND DISADVANTAGES OF DIFFERENT POPULATIONS

High Densities – Over 29000 per hectare

Advantages

- The highest yields are achieved with high densities.
- High densities – 36000 per hectare – are quite acceptable for crops planted after the end of March if adequate labour is available.

Disadvantages

- Labour inputs will have to be higher and/or more skilled.
- There can be some loss of early crop in poor light years due to plant competition.

Problems can arise with Guernsey Arch training methods when overhead work is taking place.

Fruit size can be smaller. This is not necessarily a disadvantage and size can be influenced by varietal choice.

Low Densities – below 25000 per hectare

Advantages

- Low labour inputs.
- Early crop performance is often better in poor light years.

Disadvantages

- Yields are lower for long season crops.
- Fruit size can be too large for market requirement.

Plant losses due to disease, silvering or labour damage have a greater effect on final yield.

Medium Densities 25-29000 per hectare

These combine the advantages and disadvantages. For this reason they are a compromise and are often chosen!

PLANTING ARRANGEMENT

In-Row Spacings (mm) at Various Populations

Plant populations per planted hectare	Distance(m) centre to centre double rows			
	1.5	**1.6**	**1.7**	**1.8**
20000	667	625	588	556
22000	606	568	535	505
24000	556	521	490	463
26000	513	481	452	427
28000	476	446	420	397
30000	444	417	392	370
32000	417	391	368	347
34000	392	369	346	–

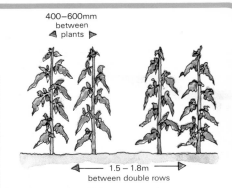

400–600mm between plants

1.5 – 1.8m between double rows

The aim should be to provide maximum light interception by plants.

An alternative to the single long season crop. Objectives are to maintain or increase vigour and yield while reducing labour for trimming and training using simpler training methods. The system should give continuous harvesting.

POINTS TO CONSIDER WHEN CONTEMPLATING INTERPLANTING

- Integration of the system into current nursery practice.
- Quality and availability of labour.
- Suitability of greenhouse for training systems.
- Scheduling for continuous harvesting.

- Desired length of crop.
- Plant density and arrangement to minimise competition between plantings.
- Method, cost and source of propagated plants.

Crop Scheduling

For any multicropping system to work successfully a carefully constructed schedule of sowing, planting, stopping and replanting dates are required:–

- Know the cropping period duration and its place in a possible crop rotation.
- The number of crops required for continuous cropping during this period with or without extension growth past the height of the top wire.

To achieve continuity the first truss of the follow-on crop should coincide with the last on the preceding crop.

The timings illustrated are only an approximate guide and will vary for various parts of the country.

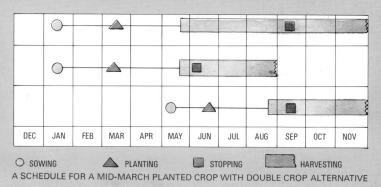

| | DEC | JAN | FEB | MAR | APR | MAY | JUN | JUL | AUG | SEP | OCT | NOV |

○ SOWING   △ PLANTING   ▣ STOPPING   ▭ HARVESTING

A SCHEDULE FOR A MID-MARCH PLANTED CROP WITH DOUBLE CROP ALTERNATIVE

PLANT ARRANGEMENT

Wider spacing of the first crop should be possible as early yield is less affected by plant density than total yield. Stopping the first crop increases early yield. Both factors reduce light competition on the replacement crop. Normally only 2 crops are grown. The second can be planted closer if the cropping system allows. Beefsteak varieties which are not economic for very early crops are often grown as interplants. The second crop can be raised from cuttings. This shortens the propagation period and improves the accuracy of planning for continuity. The young plants tend to stretch, therefore the old crop should be de-leafed hard or trained to separate wires to allow maximum light for the new crop. The use of growth regulants is being examined.

Tomatoes demand routine growth control operations throughout the growing period. After planting, the crop requires attention every 10-14 days, and in mid-summer at least every 7 days.

DE-LEAFING

De-leafing is usually a separate task from side-shooting and training. It begins just prior to start of picking and continues as a routine operation throughout the season.

A De-leafing Guide

- At least 1.2m length of stem with leaf should remain on the plant throughout the growing period.
- Excessive de-leafing reduces the photosynthetic area and affects yield and quality.
- The amount of leaf left will depend on the height of the top wire and the training system adopted.
- Remove leaves by hand using a sharp upward movement, breaking off the leaf at the petiole abcission layer. Do not use a knife; the stubs are readily infected by *Botrytis* and other diseases. Drop the leaves in the path and leave to wilt before removal. This reduces weight and bulk.
- Remove all senescent leaves, especially lower down, to encourage free air movement.
- De-leaf prior to application of a fungicide to minimise pathogen activity on leaf scar tissue.
- When using parasites as biological control agents for white fly, make sure the wasps have emerged from the parasitised scales before removal.
- Leaves will need removal to assist training. This is particularly important if layering from a low wire, and for Guernsey Arch training overhead, when leaves under the arch are taken off.
- Remove leaves for easier picking, but not beyond a truss with ripening fruit. Exposure of fruit to direct sunlight at this stage can give quality problems.
- Once the crop has been stopped, removing more leaf will encourage ripening. This also reduces shading in intercropping systems.

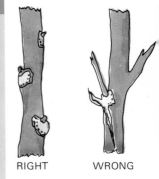

RIGHT   WRONG

WHITE FLY PARASITE

⬭ non parasitised scales

⬬ parasitised scales

◉ parasitised scales from which wasps have emerged

SIDE SHOOTING

This starts at the planting (or flowering) stage, taking care not to snap off the tender main shoot. It is particularly important to remove **all truss side shoots** to encourage strong truss development. Side shooting is part of the weekly training programme. Side shoots must never exceed 50mm (length) before removal by hand, not with a knife. Long side shoots reduce yield.

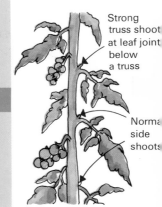

Strong truss shoot at leaf joint below a truss

Normal side shoots

POLLINATION

The object in growing tomatoes is to maximise yield of high quality fruit. Each flower must be correctly pollinated.

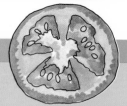

Good set, high seed count = quality fruit

POLLINATION IDEALS

- Grow the plant to produce strong, bold flowers that set readily. Each truss should carry the maximum number of viable flower buds and should continue to expand and develop rather than weaken after a few buds have formed.
- Each flower bud should develop, open and set normally.
- Each fruit on early crops (when tomatoes sell at £1000 per ton) is worth at least 5p.

Problems

If the flowering truss fails to develop normally several factors should be checked. **Excessive vigour** – especially when associated with poor light – can cause trusses to abort. **Checks to growth** – through dryness, incorrect nutrition, root pathogens, aerial pollutants – all affect truss development, flower number and quality. Day temperatures – once flowering starts – should **not** fall below 18°C.

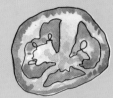

Poor set, low seed count = mis-shapen fruit

The Tomato Flower

No cross pollination occurs in tomatoes. The stigma cannot be pollinated until the pollen is released from the anthers. The stigma is in a receptive condition for longer than the pollen remains viable.

Cultural Principles to Maximise Pollination

Under ideal conditions, tomatoes self pollinate. However, we grow them in an artificial environment, at times of the year when light is poor and/or day length short. There are basic conditions

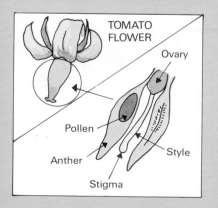

TOMATO FLOWER

Ovary

Pollen

Anther

Style

Stigma

for maximum pollination –

- Day temperatures should exceed 18°C.
- Moving the truss moves pollen from anthers to stigma. (This shortens the time that pollen remains viable).

Methods

1. Knocking each flowering truss with a strong **water jet**. Overhead irrigation systems will not move trusses.

2. Using an **electric bee** to vibrate the flowers on the lower trusses.

Damping down, especially in sunny weather, increases humidity which helps setting.

Carry out pollination operations around midday when temperatures reach 20°C. Plants will be reasonably dry when workers return from lunch.

Hormone sprays are used where pollination has failed but fruit is usually inferior to those that develop normally. If flowers mis-set, plants become vigorous; all the energy goes into stem and leaf production. This often occurs in poor light periods with incorrect temperature, watering and nutrition.

After all the effort and expense put into production it is essential that fruit is handled carefully.

FREQUENCY OF HARVESTING

- Pick at least 3 times a week (especially in hot weather). Some growers pick up to 6 times a week to satisfy specialist market requirements.
- In warm weather, pick as soon as the fruit turns from green to orange.
- Some people are wholly or partially red:green colour blind. Make certain they are not part of the harvesting, grading or marketing operation.
- Pick to a uniform colour grade. This speeds up grading and improves presentation.
- Avoid damage by fingers. Keep the calyx connected to the fruit. Its presence improves appearance and is a measure of freshness.
- Pick as early as possible in the morning and transfer to a covered trailer outside the greenhouse, or direct to a cool pack-house. Tomatoes stacked in a greenhouse rapidly overheat and quickly deteriorate. Ideally, cool the fruit to 12°C as soon as possible but take care to avoid condensation due to a sudden increase in temperature after removal.

Picking Containers

Pick into rigid containers which should be padded to avoid bruising and damage. Strong picking bags holding about 8 kg allow both hands free for picking. Buckets and baskets reduce picking speed. Transfer fruit in containers to the packhouse; or empty into larger transporting units. If fruit is soft, bulk quantities should be kept small and no container should be overfilled.

Picking containers

Picking Trolleys

A range of models can be pushed by knee or hand between the rows. Others have rollers and run on heating pipes between rows. Battery operated trolleys add a further degree of sophistication. Lightweight metal stilts attached to footwear can be useful in houses with high wires.

Picking Rates

Rates of picking depend on stage of crop and skill of staff, varying between 100 kg–170 kg per worker per hour. Greenhouse layout and training systems also influence speed. Double rows should not exceed 30m long; it is time consuming to go up and down rows repeatedly. Aim at a training system that presents the fruit at a convenient height for pickers and avoids stretching and bending.

Mobile steps

CHEMICAL RIPENING

The product **Ethrel C** (2 chloroethylphosphonic acid) speeds ripening by releasing ethylene directly to the plant tissues, and saves time and labour, at the end of the season. Treated fruit ripens on the plant and does not need 'bench ripening'. Plants can be pulled out earlier, giving more time for soil sterilising, or earlier planting of following crops. Leaves will be damaged if used indiscriminately during the early growth stages.

How to Use Ethrel C

- A minimum air temperature of 16°C is needed for best results.

- Use 1 litre in 1000 litres of water per hectare.

- Apply as an overall spray, thoroughly wetting all the fruit.

- Take care to avoid spray drift on to other crops.

- The material is acidic, observe the safety recommendations on the label.

NB Incorrect use can affect shelf life and fruit colour.

Suggested Programme of Application of Ethrel C

Days before pulling out	Action
19	Thoroughly water the borders.
18	De-leaf to expose the fruit; pick hard.
17	Spray with Ethrel C.
12	The fruit will start to ripen. Allow 5 clear days after spraying before picking.

Ethrel C is cleared under the Pesticides Safety Precaution Scheme but is not approved under the Agricultural Chemicals Approval Scheme. Instructions given on the product label, must be followed and all treatments are at 'growers risk'.

TRANSPORT FROM GREENHOUSE TO PACKING SHED

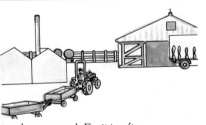

Tomatoes deteriorate relatively quickly. Move fruit quickly from 'hot' greenhouse to 'cool' pack-house. Systems of transport depend on the size of the business.

The Transport Options

- On smaller nurseries, trolleys or motorised trucks are used. Fruit is often transported in the containers used for picking. On level concrete roads, one man can handle up to ⅓ tonne.

- Simple railway trucks may be used on suitable layouts.

- Picking containers can be emptied into large trays or bulk bins containing not more than ⅓ tonne firm fruit. The system can be palletised or tractor drawn trolleys can be used.

- From the picking containers, fruit is emptied on to power operated belts for direct movement into the packhouse and grading machinery. New methods are evolving using water flotation processes to transfer fruit to conveyors and then to grading machinery. This has the advantage of cooling fruit and removing dirt and spray residues but moisture must be removed before grading.

GRADING

The aim is to ensure that a consistent sample is marketed, accurately described and one upon which the customer can rely. A well designed packing shed allows a day's output to be packed with minimum delay and fewest operators.

PACKHOUSE LAYOUT AND DESIGN

- The packhouse should be near the growing house(s), preferably in a central position.
- There must be easy access for lorries.
- Size is decided by peak daily throughput, and storage requirements.
- Work flow is based on reception, grading, packing and despatch.

- Grading, sizing and packing are continuous operations. The entire operation cannot proceed faster than the slowest stage.
- A large range of grades and containers reduces efficiency and increases space requirements.
- Work rate of skilled staff is limited by inferior layout and equipment.

SIZE AND QUALITY

Tomatoes must be carefully graded for quality and size.

There are 4 main quality standards:
EXTRA CLASS – superior quality – the target class but seldom used.
CLASS I – Good quality, the main market grade.
CLASS II – reasonable quality.
CLASS III – Poorest gradable quality – not always marketed.

There are associated sizing criteria – CLASS I (compulsory) and CLASS II (optional). The aim must be for at least 85% Class I fruit. Classes cover requirements for the Round, Semi-Ribbed and Ribbed fruit which appears on the UK Market.

Basically all fruit must be clean, free from deposits, reasonably firm and free from all but slight skin defects.

GRADING MACHINERY

Quality grading is best tackled from a flow of fruit over a series of rollers or solid belting. Speed depends on the skill of operators and quality of fruit.

Size grading is carried out on the main part of the machine. Output varies from 1200 kg to 8 tonnes per hour. Colour grading using electronic 'eyes' as part of size grading is justified on large businesses.

Market Containers

Containers should protect fruit at all times, and be attractive. The two British Standard specifications (6 kg) – Non-returnable fibreboard trays – BS 3789 : 1975 Non-returnable wooden trays – BS 2892 : 1974

Storage

- The ripening process in tomatoes can be delayed, but never stopped.
- Do not store tomatoes with crops susceptible to ethylene, eg cucumbers.
- Short term storage – 1 or 2 days – is the period of most interest to growers. Overnight storage will aid labour management and distribution.
- Fast removal of field heat to a steady 7-10°C will improve shelf life. Some outlets now demand fruit at these temperatures.
- Conventional refrigerated stores or ice-bank coolers can be used.

MARKETING

SUPPLY AND DEMAND

The marketing of tomatoes is highly competitive. During the home production season they are imported from Holland, the Channel Islands, Canary Isles, Spain and Eire. Produce from these countries is well presented in attractive packs and well promoted. Growers must be fully aware of market requirements and meet these to obtain maximum prices. Home producers have to compete against a fairly static home demand. At present imports account for 40% of consumption during the main season. Total supplies on the UK market are 14% higher than they were 7-8 years ago from March to October and 20% up in March and April. Western European production increased by 10-20%, 1981-1982 – in part this was a seasonal effect.

WHAT ARE THE OUTLETS?

Wholesale Market

This is the traditional method of marketing. Containers, transport costs, commission charges and porterage have all to be deducted from the growers' return. A range of containers is used. Despite some movement away from this outlet, it remains of prime importance across the marketing scene as a whole.

Pre-packer

Most pre-packers specify graded produce or at least produce that has been selectively picked. In some instances, pre-packers collect tomatoes direct from the nursery and supply containers for the produce – thus allowing growers to concentrate all efforts into production.

The pre-packer has sophisticated grading and packing lines dealing with a multiplicity of outlets and requirements. To be profitable these lines must run continuously and growers with small production units have to develop a group approach to meet quantity and quality requirements of pre-packers.

Multiple Store

Large growers or groups of growers may supply graded and packed produce direct to a multiple store depot or an individual store. Around 25% of total supplies are sold by this method. They demand stringent quality standards and continuity.

Co-operatives and Central Grading Establishments

Produce from the nursery is sent to a distribution depot or central packhouse for quality grading, sizing and packing prior to despatch. Grouping, creating greater scale of operations merits further expansion. Increased supply allows the planning and achievement of programmes meeting the needs of several outlets, especially chain stores. Consistent quality and continuity of supply is vital to give a financial 'edge' to individuals and the group.

Farm Shop

Direct sales to the public attract a premium and are of greatest value to the small producer. Marketing and packaging costs are low and customers receive a personal service. Retailing time and limitations on quality sold can be a problem.

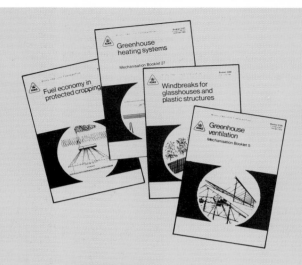

There are many free specialised ADAS publications to help and guide tomato growers towards successful production. Single copies are obtainable from MAFF offices or by post from MAFF Publications, Lion House, Willowburn Estate, Alnwick, Northumberland, NE66 2PF.

Greenhouses are an expensive investment and require protection especially from wind. B2284 **Windbreaks for glasshouses and plastic structures** gives constructional and siting detail. B2105 **Greenhouse Ventilation** shows methods of installing and improving greenhouse ventilation.

An enormous amount of equipment is necessary for the correct functioning of the modern greenhouse. Water quality is described in L776 and irrigation equipment in B2140. Fuel is a major cost and B2127 **Greenhouse heating systems**, B2114 **Boilers for nursery use**, and B2223 **Fuel economy in protected cropping** concentrate on this important aspect.

Aspects of packing and grading are covered in L714 **Horticultural packing sheds**, and L819 **Lighting and operator skills in grading horticultural produce.**

B2243 **Control of pests and diseases of protected crops – Tomatoes** is regularly updated.

Finally, the Electricity Council produce excellent technical sheets on all aspects of lighting. These are obtainable from: The Farm Electric Centre, National Agricultural Centre, Stoneleigh, Kenilworth, Warwickshire, CV8 2LS.

Printed in the UK for HMSO
Dd 736420 C100 9/83